All Aboard! The *Belle of Louisville*

By Marie Bradby

Illustrated by Annette Cable

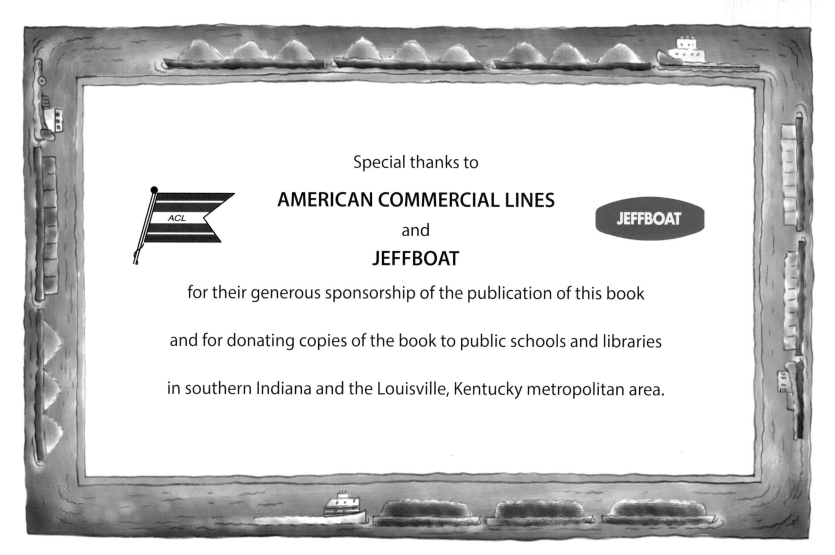

Special thanks to

AMERICAN COMMERCIAL LINES

and

JEFFBOAT

for their generous sponsorship of the publication of this book

and for donating copies of the book to public schools and libraries

in southern Indiana and the Louisville, Kentucky metropolitan area.

Acknowledgements

Thanks to Captain Doty, Linda Harris, Captain Fitzgerald, and all the crew and staff of the *Belle of Louisville* for being so nice.
Merci beaucoup à Marlene Grissom, of the Waterfront Development Corporation.
Loving thanks to Stanley and Julia Bradby—the best parents ever—for their support.

Marie Bradby grew up in the Washington, D.C. area watching boats on the Potomac River. She began writing stories when she was seven. Her previous books include *More Than Anything Else* and *Some Friend*. Learn more about Marie at www.mariebradby.com

Annette Cable grew up on a dairy farm in central Ohio. She began to draw to entertain her daredevil, wild little brothers. Her book, *The Ice Cream Hotel*, is yummy. Learn more about Annette at www.etsy.com/shop/annettecableart

Summary: A group of characters take a ride on the historic steamboat, the *Belle of Louisville* (built in 1914), and go on a journey back in time.

Designed by Annette Cable

Printed in Canada
Manufactured by Friesens Corporation in Altona, MB, Canada in October 2013
Job # 89457
ISBN Number: 978-1-935497-79-0
Library of Congress Control Number: 2013951074

Published by:
Marie Brady and Annette Cable
Produced by:
Butler Books
www.butlerbooks.com

The next time you see an ACL towboat pushing barges along the river, give them a wave!

dedicated to Dennis (always) – M.B.

dedicated to Mark and Izzy ♥ – A.C.

They say you can hear the calliope whistle for miles.

In Louisville, Kentucky, this busy city of dreams
that sits on a curve beside the mighty Ohio River,
the calliope whistle plays its cheerful songs,
beckoning people onto the oldest operating
Mississippi River-style steamboat in the world.

It's the *BELLE of LOUISVILLE.*

Gita puts down her book on the most interesting girl in the world.

Sean down in Shively will fix the porch railing another day.

Leonard grabs his hat.

Tiffany in the Highlands rushes out of her ballet lesson.

$x+6=10$

$49=(3x+8)^2$

$\sqrt{49}=$

$7=3x+$

Raj will solve his math problem tomorrow.

$x+6=10$

$(x+6)-6=(10)-6$

$x=4$

LaLaLa LaLaLa LaLaLa LaLaLa LaLaLa LaLaLa

CLANG!

Madame Foo-Foo stops
singing at the opera.

GROCERY

Chuck in
St. Matthews quits
cutting salami.

Can you hear the music?

Jason in Jeffersonville jogs
across the Big Four Bridge.

hurry... hurry... hurry...

The calliope (ka-LIE-oh-pea) is a rare musical instrument that sends steam through large whistles. Sometimes it is called the steam piano. It is very loud. The off-pitch notes sound like a combination of a flute and an organ. You have to press really hard on the metal keys.

Hurry! The calliope is calling people to board the *Belle*.

Just follow the music to the Fourth Street Wharf to see this magnificent, marvelous, majestic steamboat.

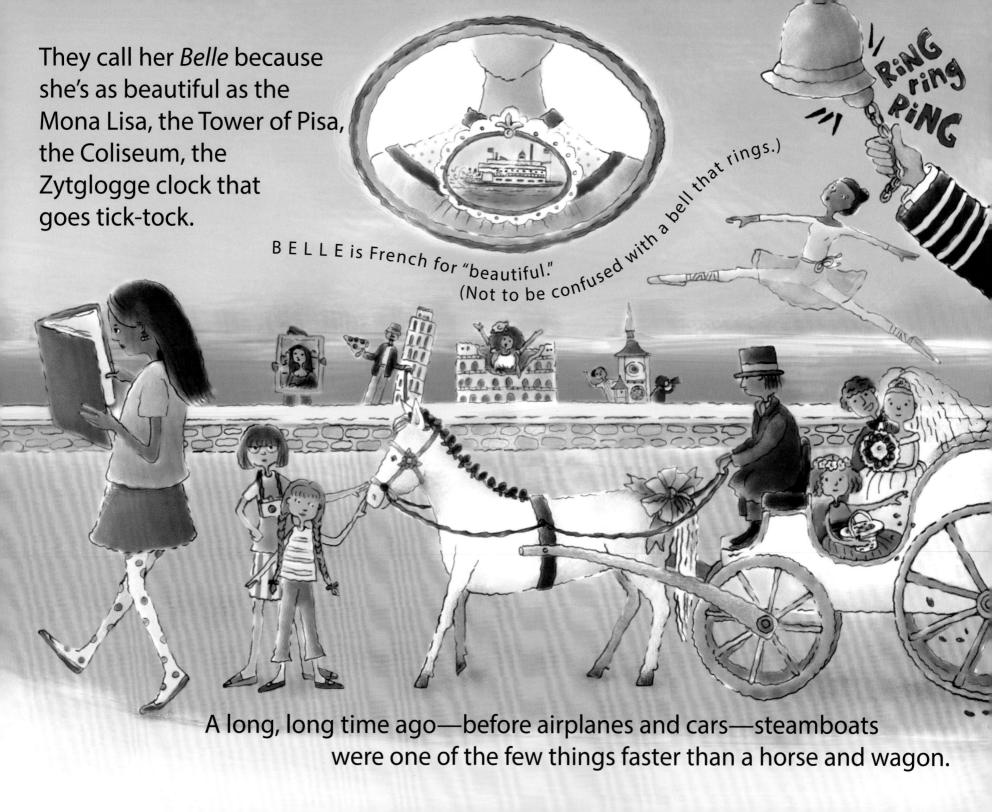

They call her *Belle* because she's as beautiful as the Mona Lisa, the Tower of Pisa, the Coliseum, the Zytglogge clock that goes tick-tock.

B E L L E is French for "beautiful." (Not to be confused with a bell that rings.)

RiNG ring RiNG

A long, long time ago—before airplanes and cars—steamboats were one of the few things faster than a horse and wagon.

Head up the grand staircase and witness this wondrous machine.

"Tickets, please! Tickets, please!"

Settle into a chair on the "hurricane" deck
or wave from a table on the "Texas" deck.

Can you feel the rumble of the engines?

Welcome aboard!

says Captain Mark Doty. He's in charge. He makes sure that everyone travels safely. He tells everyone where to find life jackets. He urges people to use the handrails and says, "Don't throw anything into the river," (not even your gum wrapper).

From the wing-bridge, Captain Doty gives directions to the crew.

"Are you ready?" he radios.

"Ready," the crew answers.

"Back her out slow."

"Backing out slow."

"Let the stern lines go."

The *striker* in the engine room opens the throttle and puts the boat in reverse.

The *deckhands* untie the dock lines and push off.

On the top deck, the *pilot* carefully steers the boat away from the dock. He's got the eyes of an eagle. Boy, can he spin that big wheel!

The *fireman* turns up the boiler to make more steam, the ship's power.

The *pilot* blows the whistle. One long. Three short.

Cover your ears!

TOOOOOOOOT! TOOT! TOOT! TOOT!

(Not even Madame Foo-Foo at the opera can sing that loud!)

(L'amour est un oiseau rebelle...)

bon voyage...

Captain Doty signals the big indicator for "Full Speed Ahead."

Below deck, the *striker* switches gears to "forward."

And we're off!

Leonard and some old geezers head straight to the engine room— that dizzying array of gears, pipes, motors, shafts, cranks, dials, wheels, and tools.

The big engine pistons begin to pound.

SWOOOSH! SWOOOSH! SWOOOSH!

Steam PUFFS.
        Motors WHIRR.
                Gears CLICK.
Engineers oil moving parts.

The big paddlewheel turns faster and faster.

How a Steamboat Works
by Raj

Water is heated in a boiler to make steam. Steam that is pumped into the engine pushes the pistons. The piston moves the Pitman arm. The Pitman operates the crank. The crank turns the paddlewheel. The paddlewheel goes round and round, and propels the boat through the water.

Flags fly.

Hold on to your hats!

Here we go!

The *Belle* heads northeast, up the big Ohio River.

There are boats everywhere.

Tugboats, barges, motor boats, sailboats, Coast Guard boats, speedboats, yachts, fishing boats, row boats, rubber ducks.

When speedboats zoom by, they make huge waves and it can get really rocky and bumpy on most boats.

WHOA!

WHOA!

SQUEAK

SQUEAK

SQUEAK

WHOA!

Whoa!

But not on the *Belle*.

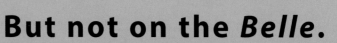

None of the other boats is like the *Belle*

with her gingerbread trim,

her twin smokestacks,

her grand ballroom,

her big red paddlewheel.

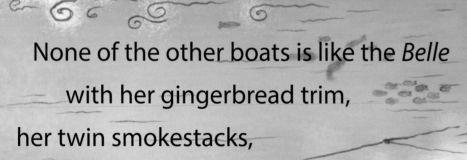

She just takes her time and rolls smoothly along,
like the beautiful lady she is.

For Mortimer and Miles, this is a journey back in time.

First named
the *Idlewild*,
the *Belle* was built in 1914,
in Pittsburgh, Pennsylvania,
way before even Mortimer's
great-great Aunt Nellie was born.

"Back then, everyone wore hats
and had a cow in the backyard,"
Mortimer tells Miles.

The *Idlewild* was sent
south to carry cotton,
tobacco, people, and even pigs across the
Mississippi River between
Memphis, Tennessee, and West
Memphis, Arkansas.

"There wasn't a bridge then," Miles tells
Mortimer, "but there was the blues."

By 1931, the *Idlewild* couldn't find much work. With more trains, trucks, and highways, steamboats weren't needed anymore for hauling. So she became an excursion boat, taking people out on short cruises.

She ended up in Louisville, running trips back and forth to an amusement park along the Ohio River.

During the war, she worked as a tugboat, pushing barges all day up and down the Mississippi River.

At night, soldiers danced onboard to the sounds of big bands.

"Man, those cats could really swing," says Miles.

After the war, she left Louisville, and was renamed the *Avalon*. She "tramped" up and down the Western Rivers, from Stillwater, Minnesota to New Orleans, Louisiana, from Pennsylvania to Nebraska, picking up riders who wanted to escape the summer heat.
"You could take a ride for five cents," says Mortimer.

Most steamboats only lasted a few years, but the *Avalon* kept going and going. She worked hard and became run-down and abandoned.

Her parts were being sold off, even her original steam calliope. She was headed to the scrap heap.

But the people of Louisville saved her. In 1962, the county bought her at auction, rebuilt her decks, overhauled her old engines, repainted her inside and out, and cleaned her up until . . . she looked as shiny as a new silver dollar.

She was renamed **"The Belle of Louisville".** . . .

Mr. and Mrs. Feathers have been married for fifty years and they still like each other.

School is out, school is in.

Your cousin is visiting from Omaha, Nebraska.

Your grandpa came all the way from India.

TREASURE ISLAND

. . . . It means **"The Beauty of Louisville."**

People ride this boat of dreams to celebrate.

Mrs. Petridish just retired after teaching biology for forty years.

Whatever you're celebrating, whatever makes you jump for joy . . . just enjoy the ride.

Leonard just loves the river and this machine.

Aunt Zelma is treating you to a ride because you memorized your multiplication tables.

Oscar can wiggle his tongue between his front teeth.

Timothy turned five years old.

Chloe won a contest for the longest braid.

When you leave behind the noisy city,
the world becomes just trees, water, and birds.

Except for the sound of the engines
and the water cascading off the paddlewheel,

it's as quiet

as the cool breeze

on your face

on this hot day.

You feel like you are part of this boat,

part of the river,

part of the earth.

While you are on the hurricane deck, daydreaming
about being a fish,
the *engineer* is watching the gauges on the engine,
the *fireman* is checking the pressure on the boiler,
(Gosh, is it hot in there!)
the *pilot* is watching out for other boats,
Captain Doty is talking to the passengers.

People buy souvenirs at the gift shop.
They get popcorn at the snack bar.
They watch the pistons
go back and forth.

CLICK!
CLACK!

SWOOOSH!
SWOOOSH!

All this traveling makes people hungry.

Arthur has brought an arugula and peanut butter
sandwich for his brown-bag lunch.

Fortunately,
the *Belle* has the best fried chicken in town,
plus green beans, mashed potatoes,
salads, hot rolls, apple pie,
and—for Timothy—birthday cake.

Afterwards,
 in the grand ballroom,
 everyone DANCES.

Near Six Mile Island,
the *Belle* turns around.

Leonard and others rush
to the rail to watch.

For a few moments,
the giant red paddlewheel
turns in reverse.

Then she switches gears
and chugs forward,
back to the city.

But the adventure on the *Belle* isn't over yet.

Erica sees a rare bird. (Is that a Short-billed Dowitcher?)

Raphael proposes to Maya.

Will YOU Be MINE?

Vincent knows now that he can do a triple axel in ice skating.

Caitlyn drops her ice cream cone.

Louis spots an enormous catfish.

Samantha gets an idea.

Pietra paints a masterpiece.

Leonard loses his hat.

Yes, life is full of ups and downs, just like the life of the *Belle*.

How To Save the World
by Samantha
• BE KIND.
• Always Say Thank you
• Cover your mouth
  when you sneeze.
• Eat your peas.
• Don't throw trash
  in the river.

The *deckhands* get the lines ready.

"Slow to half speed," Captain Doty radios.

"Slowing to half speed,"
says the *striker*.

"Swing her around."

"Swinging her around,"
says the *pilot*,
as he spins the giant wheel.

The *mate* tosses the line to shore.

Captain Doty blows the whistle.

TOOOOOOOOT! TOOT! TOOT! TOOT!

People take photos, shake hands, and hug their new friends goodbye.

"So long! It was nice to meet you."

It's always hard to say goodbye.

You say hello to your family and kiss them and your dog,
like you've been gone for months,
though it's only been two hours. (Sheesh!)

"Sorry about your hat," Leonard's mother says.
"It's all right, I can get another one."
"Did you have a good time?"
"It was awesome!"